Classics

Volume Twenty One

MY TWENTY FIRST CLASSIC COLLECTION
CONTAINS:

TALK TO THE PAW

WHATEVER!

WASSUP?

JIM DAVIS

First published by Ravette Publishing 2011.

Printed and bound in Great Britain
for Ravette Publishing Limited
PO Box 876
Horsham
West Sussex RH12 9GH

ISBN: 978-1-84161-359-8

GARFIELD

TALK TO THE

PAW

JiM DAViS

ℛℛ

JIM DAVIS 1-24

SLAP

WHIRRRRR..

I LOVE YA, BUDDY!

ME, I'M JUST BEING A PHONY!

JIM DAVIS 2-15

SO MUCH FOR HOME BARBERING

I THOUGHT I DID A PRETTY GOOD JOB

JIM DAVIS 5-17

GARFIELD

Whatever!

JiM DAViS   ЯR

WELL, IT WASN'T EASY, BUT I GOT BOTH SHOES ON THE SAME FOOT!

IS IT ANY WONDER I SLEEP 18 HOURS A DAY?

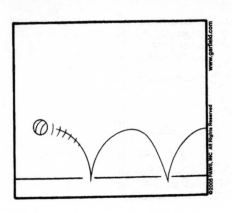

SLUP

Distributed by Universal Press Syndicate

www.garfield.com

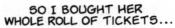

JIM DAVIS 10-20

I HAD A BAD HAIRCUT

TWO WRONGS DON'T MAKE A RIGHT, PAL!

PUT THAT TURKEY BACK!

I WAS JUST TAKING IT FOR A WALK

JIM DAVIS 11-24

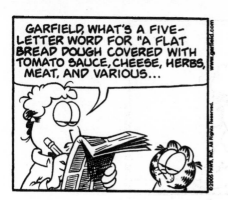

CHOMP

SLURP!

DINNER WILL BE A LITTLE LATE

"ROAST DUMMY" TAKES TIME TO PREPARE

JIM DAVIS 1-11

SCHLURP

HOW'S YOUR HOT CHOCOLATE?

FINE. AND YOURS?

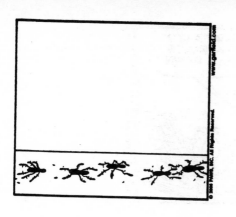

OTHER GARFIELD BOOKS AVAILABLE

Pocket Books	Price	ISBN
Am I Bothered?	£3.99	978-1-84161-286-7
Don't Ask!	£3.99	978-1-84161-247-8
Feed Me!	£3.99	978-1-84161-242-3
Gooooal!	£3.99	978-1-84161-329-1
Gotcha!	£3.50	978-1-84161-226-3
I Am What I Am!	£3.99	978-1-84161-243-0
Kowabunga	£3.99	978-1-84161-246-1
Numero Uno	£3.99	978-1-84161-297-3
S.W.A.L.K.	£3.50	978-1-84161-225-6
Talk to the Paw	£3.99	978-1-84161-317-8
Time to Delegate	£3.99	978-1-84161-296-6
Wan2tlk?	£3.99	978-1-84161-264-5
Wassup?	£3.99	978-1-84161-355-0
Whatever!	£3.99	978-1-84161-330-7
Theme Books		
Creatures Great & Small	£3.99	978-1-85304-998-9
Entertains You	£4.50	978-1-84161-221-8
Slam Dunk!	£4.50	978-1-84161-222-5
The Seasons	£3.99	978-1-85304-999-6
2-in-1 Theme Books		
All In Good Taste	£6.99	978-1-84161-209-6
Easy Does It	£6.99	978-1-84161-191-4
Lazy Daze	£6.99	978-1-84161-208-9
Licensed to Thrill	£6.99	978-1-84161-192-1
Out For The Couch	£6.99	978-1-84161-144-0
The Gruesome Twosome	£6.99	978-1-84161-143-3
Classics		
Volume One	£7.99	978-1-85304-970-5
Volume Two	£7.99	978-1-85304-971-2
Volume Three	£7.99	978-1-85304-996-5
Volume Four	£7.99	978-1-85304-997-2
Volume Five	£6.99	978-1-84161-022-1
Volume Six	£7.99	978-1-84161-023-8
Volume Seven	£7.99	978-1-84161-088-7
Volume Eight	£7.99	978-1-84161-089-4
Volume Nine	£6.99	978-1-84161-149-5
Volume Ten	£7.99	978-1-84161-150-1
Volume Eleven	£7.99	978-1-84161-175-4
Volume Twelve	£7.99	978-1-84161-176-1
Volume Thirteen	£6.99	978-1-84161-206-5
Volume Fourteen	£7.99	978-1-84161-207-2
Volume Fifteen	£5.99	978-1-84161-232-4
Volume Sixteen	£5.99	978-1-84161-233-1
Volume Seventeen	£7.99	978-1-84161-250-8
Volume Eighteen	£6.99	978-1-84161 251-5

Classics (cont'd ...)	Price	ISBN
Volume Nineteen	£6.99	978-1-84161-303-1
Volume Twenty	£6.99	978-1-84161 304-8

Gift Books

30 years - the fun's just begun	£9.99	978-1-84161-307-9
Don't Know, Don't Care	£4.99	978-1-84161-279-9
Get a Grip	£4.99	978-1-84161-282-9
I Don't Do Ordinary	£4.99	978-1-84161-281-2
Keep your Attitude, I have my own	£4.99	978-1-84161-278-2

Little Books

C-c-c-caffeine	£2.50	978-1-84161-183-9
Food 'n' Fitness	£2.50	978-1-84161-145-7
Laughs	£2.50	978-1-84161-146-4
Love 'n' Stuff	£2.50	978-1-84161-147-1
Surf 'n' Sun	£2.50	978-1-84161-186-0
The Office	£2.50	978-1-84161-184-6
Zzzzzz	£2.50	978-1-84161-185-3

Miscellaneous

Colour Collection Book 3	£11.99	978-1-84161-320-8
Colour Collection Book 2	£10.99	978-1-84161-306-2
Colour Collection Book 1	£10.99	978-1-84161-293-5
Treasury 7	£10.99	978-1-84161-248-5
Treasury 6	£10.99	978-1-84161-229-4
Treasury 5	£10.99	978-1-84161-198-3
Treasury 4	£10.99	978-1-84161-180-8
Treasury 3	£9.99	978-1-84161-142-6
How to Draw Garfield & Friends (May 2010)	£3.99	978-1-84161-334-5
Garfield & Co graphic novel (Oct 2010)	£6.99	978-1-84161-349-9

All Garfield books are available at your local bookshop or from the publisher at the address below.

Just send your order with your payment and name and address details to:-

Ravette Publishing Ltd
PO Box 876
Horsham
West Sussex RH12 9GH
(tel: 01403 711443 ... email: ingrid@ravettepub.co.uk)

Prices and availability are subject to change without notice.

Please enclose a cheque or postal order made payable to **Ravette Publishing** to the value of the cover price of the book/s and allow the following for UK postage and packing:-

70p for the first book + 40p for each additional book
except Treasuries & Colour Collections... when please add £3.00 per book